SNUG, BUG, RUG

STICKER AND DRAW

car

tree

map

cat

soc

frog

This edition published by Parragon Books Ltd in 2016

Parragon Books Ltd
Chartist House
15–17 Trim Street
Bath BA1 1HA, UK
www.parragon.com

Copyright © Parragon Books Ltd 2016

Written by Susan Fairbrother
Illustrated by Abigail Burch and Ana Seixas
Edited by Laura Baker
Designed by Karissa Santos and Clare Phillips
Consultant checked by Geraldine Taylor
Production by Charlotte McKillop

ISBN 978-1-4748-2051-6

Printed in China

house

SNUG,
BUG,
RUG

sun

pen

cloud

PaRragon

Bath · New York · Cologne · Melbourne · Delhi
Hong Kong · Shenzhen · Singapore

mop

Note:
To get the best learning out of this book, it is recommended that an adult work alongside the child.

Look, a cloud that looks like a **cat**!
Sticker other objects you can see in the clouds.

cat

flower

umbrella

tree

hat

key

Whose home is whose?
Sticker the pets!

Curly,
wurly
fur!

dog

kennel

cushion

cat

fish

bowl

hutch

Dotty spots!

rabbit

stop

Sticker all
the missing
vehicles!

car

tractor

bus

digger

go

van

A sailor went to sea, sea, sea,
To see what she could see, see, see...

bird

sail

boy

girl

map

fin

☐ bell

☐ sun

☐ tree

☐ cat

☐ fish

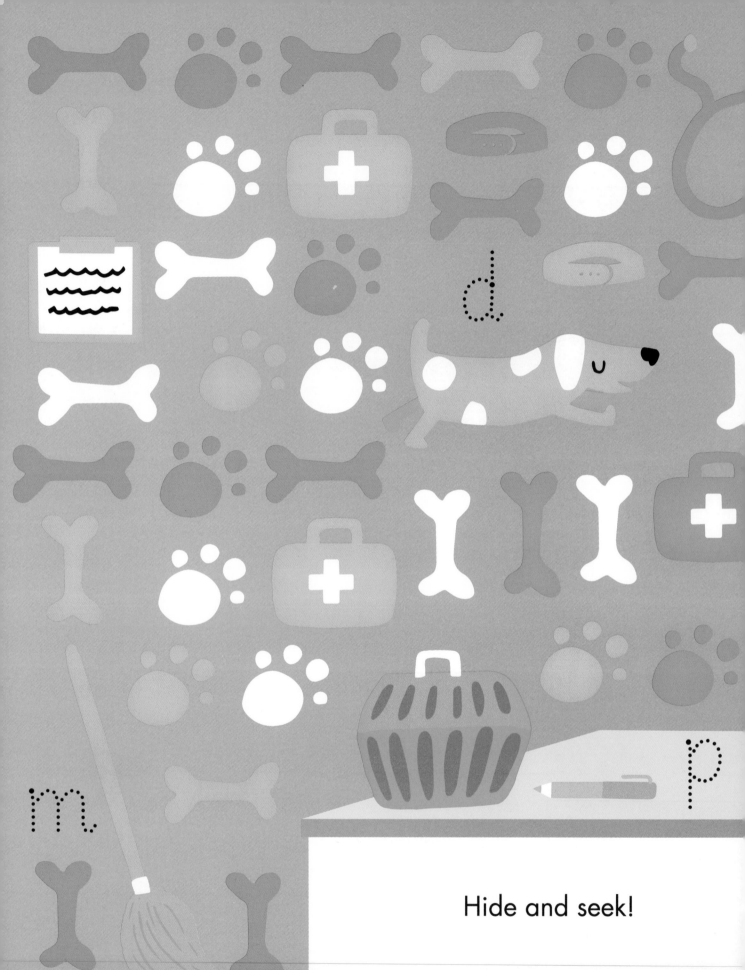

Hide and seek!

Spot and trace the letters in the picture.
Then write them here to complete these words.

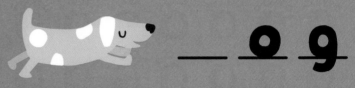 _ o g

_ a t

 _ e n

_ o p

Circle 7
red things.

boot

Fire Station

fire engine

balloon

mug

hood

stop

hose

Sticker the missing animals.

bug on a rug

dog on a log

bird in
a nest

fox in a
box

frog
on a
log!

What's the weather today?
Draw and stick.

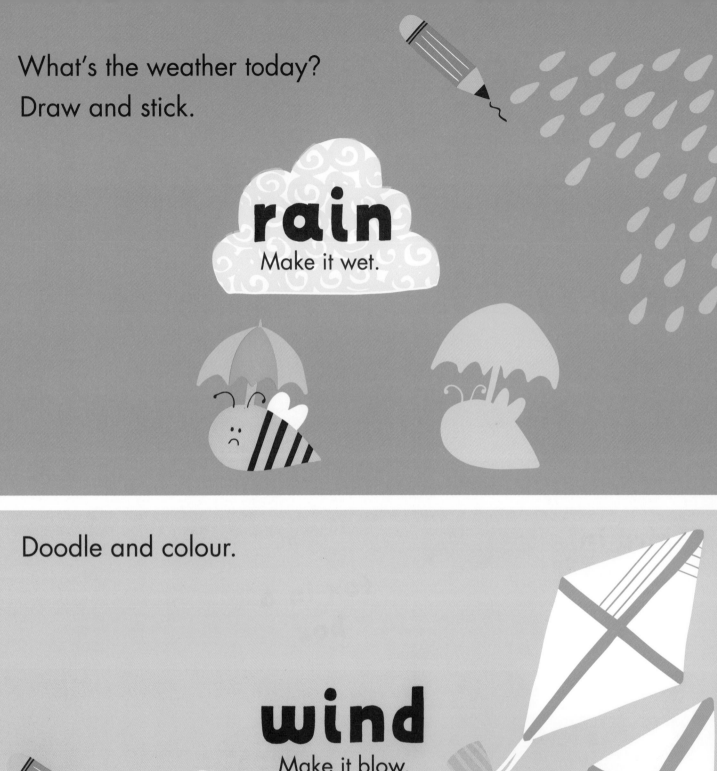

rain
Make it wet.

Doodle and colour.

wind
Make it blow.

Stick.

sun
Make it hot.

Trace.

snow
Make it snow.

Pigs **LOVE** mud.
Stick on
some splats.

pig

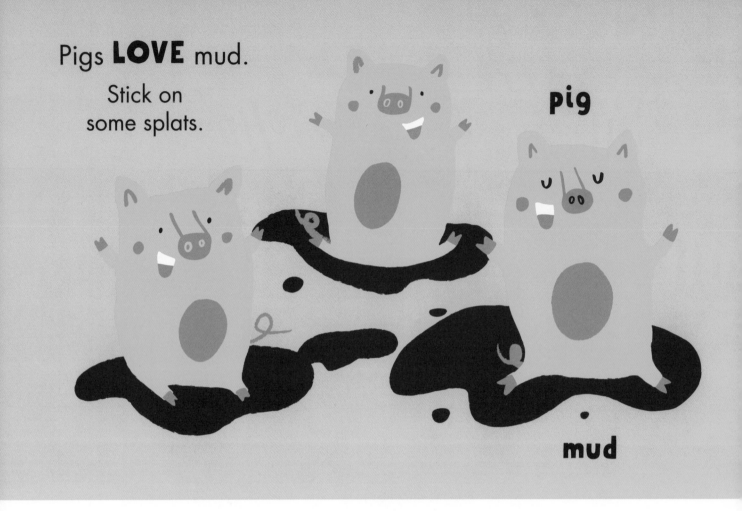

mud

Now clean them up in the **tub** with bubble stickers!

10 hens!

Count them and sticker the scenes.

1 hen on a **hill**

1 hen in a **car**

3 hens on a **bus**

2 hens under an **umbrella**

1 hen in a **boat**

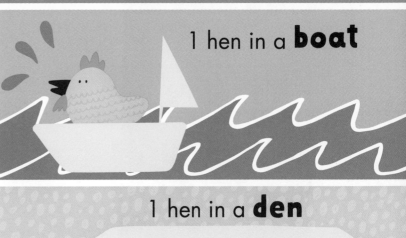

1 hen in a **den**

ZZZZZZZzzzz

1 hen in her **bed**

Ten hens in all!

Who is at the door?

It's the...

big bad
wolf!

Follow the path that leads the three little pigs to their safe brick house.

log   **house**   **tree**

5, 4, 3, 2, 1, go!

star

Sticker the stars in the sky and a rocket zooming through space.

Zoom!

rocket

Colour the
planets.

Who's on the **mat**?

cat

hat

Where is the rat's **hat**?

rat

Who's on the **plane**?

cat bat mouse

Who's **snug** on the **rug**?

bug

These sharks love to make words!

big

fin

teeth

Trace the letters and trails they have made.

Opposites camp!

Big and little

big

little

Spot and tick the opposites!

big car ☐
little car ☐

big tent ☐
little tent ☐

big fire ☐
little fire ☐

big pan ☐
little pan ☐

big kettle ☐
little kettle ☐

big flower ☐
little flower ☐

big butterfly ☐
little butterfly ☐

Welcome to the shop of many things!

pots and pans

bags

mats

fans

Sticker more items in each room.

zips

pets

wigs

(**mugs**)

Fairytale Forest

Help the princess find her way to her castle. Sticker what she sees along the wa[y]

wizard

cave

wolf

giant

Cute kittens!

They are...

warm

~~slimy~~

cuddly

scaly

cold

soft

pink

Feed the monster with stickers
and tick as you go...

smelly **cheese** and old **peas**

socks, **clocks** and **rocks**

a **bat** and a **hat**

a **shell** and a **bell**

a **mug**, a **jug** and a **rug**!

happy

Stick the faces in the right places.

sad

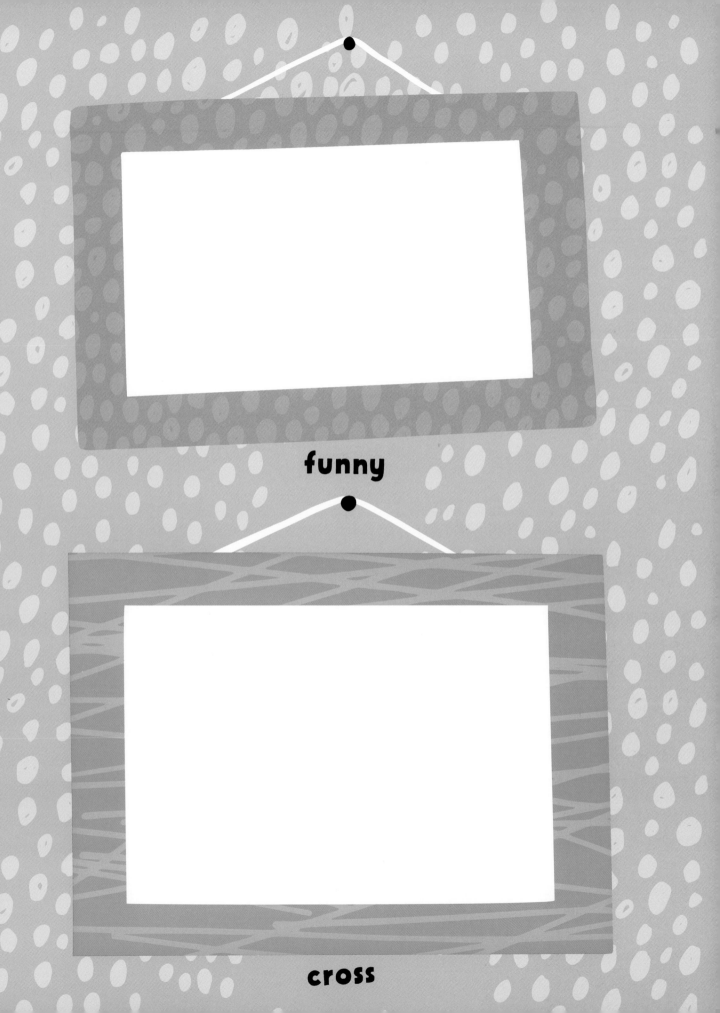

funny

cross

Presents!

Thank you for my...

bell

Thank you for my...

carrot

Thank you for my...

pen

Thank you
for my...

hat

Thank you
for my...

teddy

Thank you
for my...

bun

Does the cat look...

happy

or

sad?

Circle the right word.

He's sad!
He wants a
makeover.

How about
a **hat**?

A **cap**?

A **crown**?

No? How about a big **grin**!

Draw it on.
That's better!

king

Who is wearing
these crowns?

queen

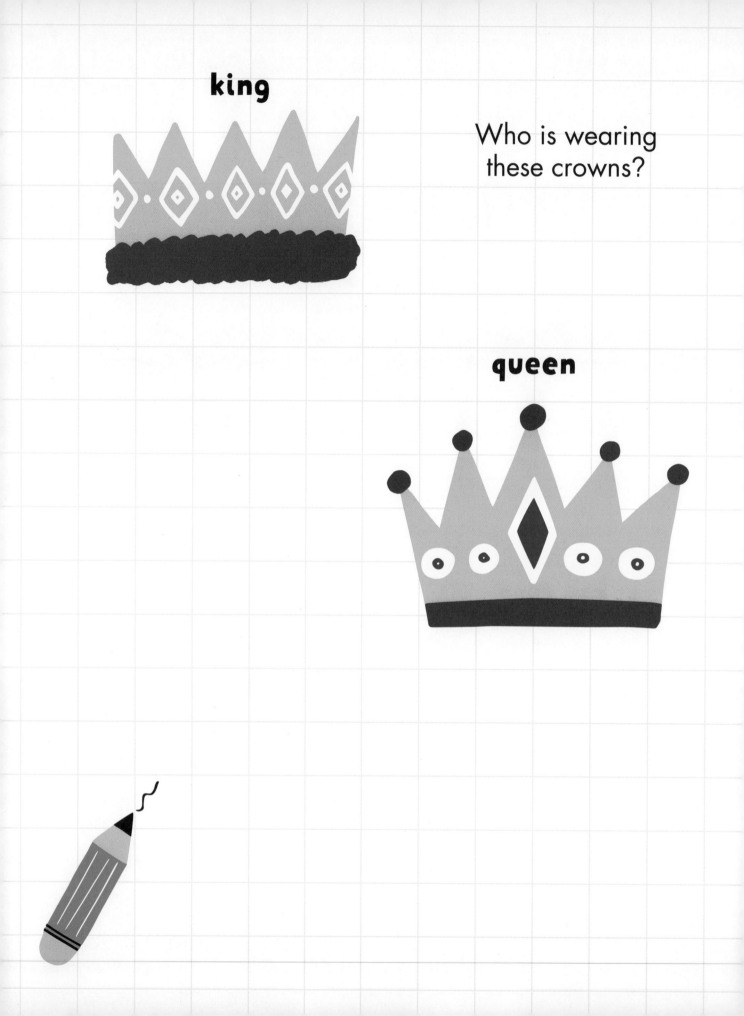

flag

Sticker the stately, shapely home of the **king** and **queen**.

window

door

flower

path

dog

tree

frog

hat

cat

car

hen

moon

sock

shell

bell